GREAT
BRITISH
landmarks

Wales

Wales may be the smallest country in the United Kingdom but it is filled with breathtaking and beautiful sights. From the white-topped mountains of Snowdonia and the green rolling valleys of the Brecon Beacons to the grey and golden weathered coastlines, there's plenty to see and do for thrill seekers and nature lovers alike.

History and truth mingle with myth and poetry in a nation shaped not only by geography but also by the language and the people. Remember the lines written by Wordsworth above the spectacular ruins of Tintern Abbey; visit historical Conwy Castle and imagine the lives of those that lived and died within the battlements; and, if you're brave enough, cross the valley near Aberystwyth where legend has it, the Devil himself was tricked.

Colour abounds in this small nation, from the grey and brown castle walls to the dramatic hues of the landscapes which change with the weather. Bring this charming country to life with your colouring pencils.

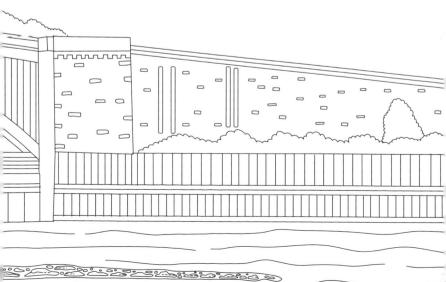

Ffestiniog Railway, Gwynedd, Wales

Tintern Abbey, Gwent, Wales

"Once again
Do I behold these steep and lofty cliffs,
That on a wild secluded scene impress
Thoughts of more deep seclusion; and connect
The landscape with the quiet of the sky."

Tintern Abbey
by William Wordsworth

Snowdonia National Park, Wales

"Cenedl heb iaith, cenedl heb galon."

*"A nation without a language
is a nation without a heart."*

Welsh Proverb

South Stack Lighthouse, Anglesey, Wales

Conwy Castle, Conwy, Wales

Devil's Bridge, Aberystwyth, Wales

"How art thou named?
In search of what strange land,
From what huge height, descending?
Can such force
Of waters issue from a British source,
Or hath not Pindus fed thee, where the band
Of patriots scoop their freedom out, with hand
Desperate as thine?"

To the Torrent at the Devil's Bridge
by William Wordsworth

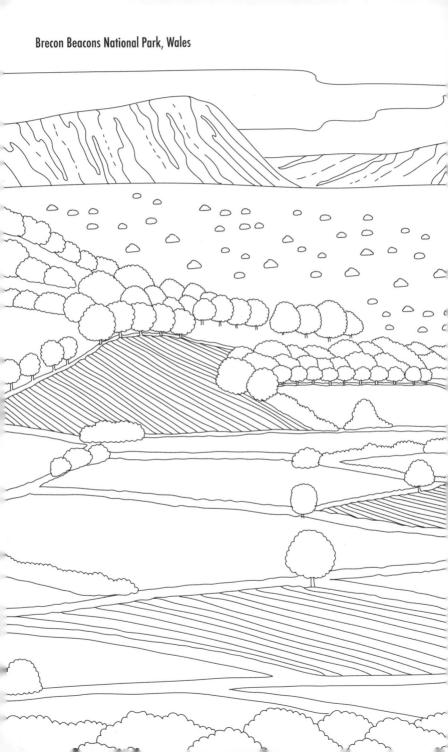

Scotland

Remote and beautiful islands, thick and mysterious woodlands, legendary lochs, lakes and rivers, golden beaches, and the United Kingdom's highest mountain; Scotland has it all. It is a land of pre-history, myth and antiquity blended with the contemporary; from the ancient standing stones of Callanish and the awe-inspiring Edinburgh Castle to the modern Kelpies sculpture in Falkirk.

Be inspired by the rolling hills and lush, green fields of the lowlands and the deep, dark glens and towering snow-capped mountains of the highlands. Explore the unique, enchanting islands and discover the colourful nature of Scotland.

Edinburgh Castle, Edinburgh, Scotland

Broch of Mousa, Shetland Islands, Scotland

"Oft wand'ring by thy sea-beat shore
I woo'd the pensive Muse:
Nor will the Genii of thy rocks
This votive lay refuse."

Address to Zetland
by Dorothea Primrose Campbell

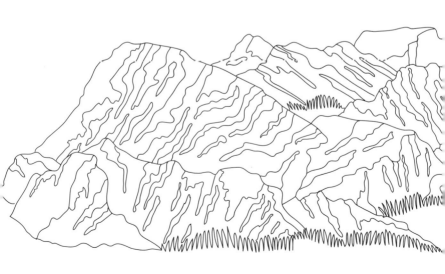

The Callanish Stones, Isle of Lewis, Outer Hebrides, Scotland

"O wad some Power the giftie gie us,
To see oursels as ithers see us!"

To A Louse
by Robert Burns

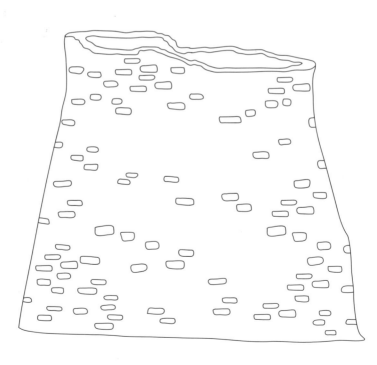

Loch Ness, Inverness, Scotland

Wallace Monument, Stirling, Scotland

"We look to Scotland for all
our ideas of civilisation."

Voltaire

Shetland Islands, Scotland

Northern Ireland

Although only accounting for a sixth of Ireland's total area, Northern Ireland is bursting with sensational history. Take a step back in time and discover the magnificent 50 million year old basalt columns of the Giant's Causeway, or learn about the tumultuous history of Dunluce castle, all while taking in Northern Ireland's breathtaking landscapes.

Get lost in the legends of this magical land. Climb its stunning mountains, stroll through the purple heather laden hills, explore astonishing coastlines, and unearth the history behind Northern Ireland's outstanding architecture.

The Dark Hedges in Ballymoney,
County Antrim, Northern Ireland

"An Irishman's heart is nothing but his imagination."

George Bernard Shaw

"May the Irish hills caress you.
May her lakes and rivers bless you.
May the luck of the Irish enfold you.
May the blessings of Saint Patrick behold you."

Irish Blessing

Dunluce Castle in Bushmills, County Antrim, Northern Ireland

Marble Arch Caves near Florencecourt,
County Fermanagh,
Northern Ireland

Mussenden Temple in Castlerock, County Londonderry, Northern Ireland

"Suave, mari magno turbantibus aequora ventis e terra magnum alterius spectare laborem."

"'Tis pleasant, safely to behold from the shore, The troubled sailor, and hear the tempests roar."

Inscription outside Mussenden Temple

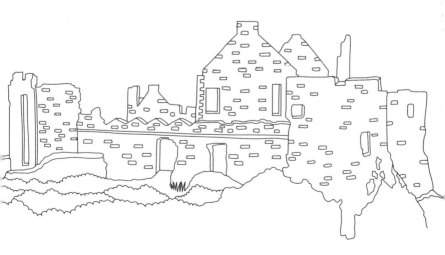

Northern England

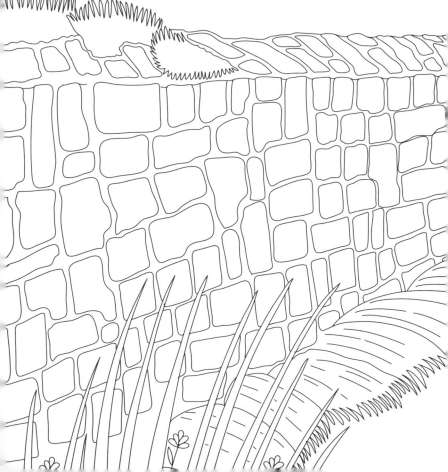

Despite being at the heart of the industrial revolution, Northern England boasts some of the most spectacular natural landscapes in the country. Discover the Roman history of Hadrian's Wall which stretches from Carlisle to Wallsend and fall in love with the Brontë's Yorkshire moors. If it's culture you're after, visit the stunning Tudor birthplace of Shakespeare, or unearth Norman history at Durham cathedral.

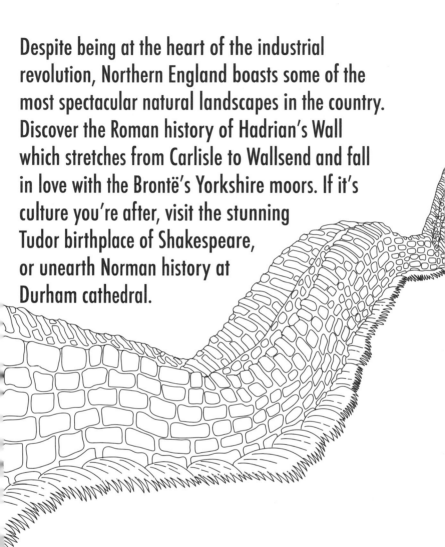

Delve into exquisite architecture – both new and old. Be transported to Ancient Athens at the Penshaw Monument, then get up close to the copper-coloured patina of Gateshead's Angel of the North, a 200 tonne steel statue dominating the Northern skyline.

Durham Cathedral, Durham, England

Penshaw Monument near Sunderland, Tyne and Wear, England

"Bright and fierce and fickle is the South,
And dark and true and tender is the North."

The Princess: O Swallow
by Alfred, Lord Tennyson

Hadrian's Wall, from Carlisle to Wallsend, England

"We are told to let our light shine, and if it does, we won't need to tell anybody it does. Lighthouses don't fire cannons to call attention to their shining – they just shine."

Dwight L. Moody

St. Mary's Lighthouse near Whitley Bay, Tyne and Wear, England

The Angel of the North near Gateshead, Tyne and Wear, England

"The greatest products of architecture are less the works of individuals than of society; rather the offspring of a nation's effort, than the inspired flash of a man of genius..."

Victor Hugo

South East England

From iconic coastlines and rolling hills to bustling streets, the South East of England offers visitors a wide and beautiful array of landscapes. Visit the historical city of Cambridge, gaze upon the crumbling white chalk cliffs of the Seven Sisters, or be overwhelmed by the colourful streets of London. There are familiar landmarks and hidden gems to discover right across this region.

History, nature and architecture work in harmony in landscapes including King's College in Cambridge and Richmond Park, London's largest Royal Park. Subdued colours of architecture and nature are contrasted with the bright lights of iconic London.

Big Ben, London, England

Windsor Castle, Berkshire, England

"Great King William stood on Windsor,
Looking from its castled height
O'er his wide-spread realm of England,
Glittering in the morning light;"

William the Conqueror
by Hezekiah Butterworth

King's College, Cambridge, Cambridgeshire, England

"Sir, when a man is tired of London,
he is tired of life; for there is in London
all that life can afford."

Samuel Johnson

Telephone box, London, England

St. Paul's Cathedral, London, England

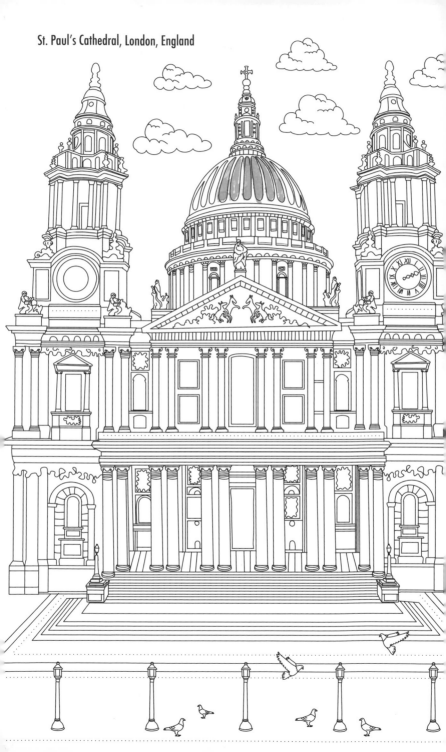

"Si monumentum requiris circumspice."

"If you seek his memorial, look around."

Epitaph on Wren's tomb
in St. Paul's Cathedral

South West England

The South West of England harbours some of the most breathtaking views in the country. A stroll along the coast of Cornwall is bound to delight with the unforgettable sight of St. Michael's Mount erupting from the sea as well as Land's End, the most westerly point in England. Marvel at the 200-foot granite cliffs carved and shaped by the waters of the English Channel, and, on a clear day, see if you can catch a glimpse of the Isles of Scilly.

Discover millennia of history as you explore the Jurassic Coast of Dorset, topped off by Durdle Door in the picturesque Lulworth Cove. Further inland you'll find Cheddar Gorge, where the grey limestone rocks jut out of the gorge's greenery. For a truly memorable experience visit Europe's best-known prehistoric monument, Stonehenge.

Cheddar Gorge, Somerset, England

Corfe Castle, Dorset, England

"My beautiful proof lies all in ruins."

Georg Cantor

Stonehenge near Amesbury, Wiltshire, England

"My soul is full of longing
For the secret of the sea,
And the heart of the great ocean
Sends a thrilling pulse through me."

The Secret of the Sea
by Henry Wadsworth Longfellow

St. Michael's Mount near Marazion, Cornwall, England

Glastonbury Tor, Somerset, England

"The Tor of Glastonbury! Even but now
I saw the hoary pile cresting the top
Of that north-western hill;"

Lewesdon Hill
by William Crowe

Land's End in Sennen, Cornwall, England